# student WORKBOOK

G000096066

# AQA AS Business Studies
## Unit 2: Managing a Business

John Wolinski and Gwen Coates

Philip Allan Updates, an imprint of Hodder Education, part of Hachette UK, Market Place, Deddington, Oxfordshire, OX15 0SE

*Orders*
Bookpoint Ltd, 130 Milton Park, Abingdon, Oxfordshire, OX14 4SB
tel: 01235 827827   fax: 01235 400401
e-mail: education@bookpoint.co.uk

Lines are open 9.00 a.m.–5.00 p.m., Monday to Saturday, with a 24-hour message answering service. You can also order through the Philip Allan Updates website: www.philipallan.co.uk

ISBN 978-0-340-97277-9

© Philip Allan Publishers 2008

Printed in Spain

Hachette UK's policy is to use papers that are natural, renewable and recyclable products and made from wood grown in sustainable forests. The logging and manufacturing processes are expected to conform to the environmental regulations of the country of origin.

This student workbook is designed to:
- guide you through the content of the new AQA Business Studies AS Unit 2: Managing a Business
- help to build your understanding of the four elements of this unit: finance; people in business; operations management; and marketing and the competitive environment
- provide you with a good set of notes on all topic areas, to help your revision

For each section of the workbook there is:
- a set of notes providing an overview of the key aspects of the AQA specification
- a variety of questions covering the main topics

Remember that you will be using this workbook to assist your revision as the examination itself approaches, so when answering the questions:
- Use the notes provided in this workbook, but enhance them by using other sources, such as your textbook(s) and notes from class sessions. Remember, the more detailed your answers, the more helpful they will be for your revision.
- Where applicable, use the context of the question (such as the industry or financial situation of the organisation) so that you are demonstrating the vital skill of application.

## Progress checklist

### Finance
**Using budgets** ☐
**Improving cash flow** ☐
**Measuring and increasing profit** ☐

### People in business
**Improving organisational structures** ☐
**Measuring the effectiveness of the workforce** ☐
**Developing an effective workforce: recruitment, selection and training** ☐
**Developing and retaining an effective workforce: motivating employees** ☐

### Operations management
**Making operational decisions** ☐
**Developing effective operations: quality** ☐
**Developing effective operations: customer service** ☐
**Working with suppliers** ☐
**Using technology in operations** ☐

### Marketing and the competitive environment
**Effective marketing** ☐
**Using the marketing mix: product** ☐
**Using the marketing mix: promotion** ☐
**Using the marketing mix: pricing** ☐
**Using the marketing mix: place** ☐
**Designing an effective marketing mix** ☐
**Marketing and competitiveness** ☐

# Using budgets

## Budgets

A **budget** is an agreed plan establishing, in numerical or financial terms, the policy to be pursued and the anticipated outcomes of that policy.

The benefits of using budgets are:
- Budgets provide direction and coordination, ensuring that spending is geared towards the aims of the business.
- Successful budgeting motivates staff, through recognition and a sense of achievement.
- Budgets improve efficiency through monitoring any successes or failures.
- They encourage accurate forecasting and thus help forward planning.

Possible drawbacks of using budgets include:
- The allocation may be inappropriate if imposed by a senior manager.
- Allocations may be incorrect because circumstances have changed.
- Keeping to a budget may not be effective — for example, if it means lowering quality.

## Variance analysis

**Variances** are differences between budgeted and actual figures. **Variance analysis** is the process by which the reasons for any variances are investigated. A **favourable variance** occurs when costs are lower than expected or revenue is higher than expected. This will lead to actual profit being higher than budgeted. An **adverse (unfavourable) variance** occurs when costs are higher than expected or revenue is lower than expected. This will lead to actual profit being lower than budgeted.

A variance is calculated by the following formula:
variance = budget figure – actual figure

For variance analysis it is best to use 'F' for favourable variances and 'A' for adverse variances, rather than positive or negative numbers.

Thus a favourable variance is shown when:
- actual revenue is greater than budgeted revenue
- actual costs are below budgeted costs

Similarly, adverse (or unfavourable) variances are shown when:
- actual revenue is less than budgeted revenue
- actual costs are above budgeted costs

After calculating variances, the budget holder will interpret their meaning. Variances may show changes in efficiency, where the business has made mistakes or improved its performance. They may also show that external influences, such as changes in the market, have made it more difficult or easier for a firm to meet its targets.

## Questions

1 Explain two benefits of using budgets.

_____

_____

2 Read the following passage.

> One week after his appointment as departmental manager, Shavri met with his section heads
> for the first time, to announce their budget allocations. He also explained the new reward
> system — any section head exceeding his or her sales target or spending less than his or her
> expenditure budget would receive a bonus based on how well the target had been hit.
>
> 'I have based these targets on last year's allocations. I have adjusted some where I think
> they are supporting the priority areas that the board of directors agreed last week. I will
> meet you monthly to monitor your sales and spending against these budgets so that I can
> see how well you are doing. At those meetings we can also discuss whether any budgets
> need to be changed in the light of circumstances.'

Evaluate the strengths and weaknesses of Shavri's approach to budgeting.

_____

_____

_____

_____

_____

_____

_____

_____

_____

_____

_____

_____

_____

_____

3 Study the following data for Layla's division and answer the questions that follow.

| | Budget (£000s) | Actual (£000s) | Variance (£000s) | F or A |
|---|---|---|---|---|
| **Sales income** | 400 | 441 | | |
| Capital costs | 56 | 88 | | |
| Raw materials | 100 | 106 | | |
| Marketing expenditure | 42 | 55 | | |
| Wages | 84 | 74 | | |
| Other costs | 40 | 40 | | |
| **Total expenditure** | | | | |
| **Profit** | | | | |

a Fill in the blank boxes in the table.

b Layla has argued that there is no need to scrutinise these results because 'the profit target has been hit'. Do you agree? Justify your view.

_____

_____

_____

_____

_____

_____

_____

c Recommend two ways in which Layla might be able to improve matters in her division. Explain your reasoning.

_____

_____

_____

_____

_____

# Improving cash flow

**Cash flow** is the movement of money into and out of an organisation over time.

## Causes of cash-flow problems

Cash-flow problems can arise because of:
- seasonal demand, leading to low cash inflows at certain times of the year
- overtrading — firms buy lots of extra materials and become short of cash
- over-investment in fixed assets, draining the company of cash
- credit sales, which may lead to a lack of cash until the credit period is over
- poor stock management, tying up cash in excessive stock levels
- paying suppliers too quickly, which can leave a business short of cash
- unforeseen changes, such as machinery breakdown, which may reduce cash holdings

## Ways of improving cash flow

Cash flow can be improved by using:
- a bank overdraft
- a short-term loan
- factoring
- selling assets
- sale and leaseback

A **bank overdraft** is an agreement whereby the holder of a current account in a bank is allowed to withdraw more money than there is in the account. Benefits of a bank overdraft are:
- It is easy to arrange and can be used to pay for whatever the business requires.
- Interest is only paid on the level of the overdraft that is actually used.
- The firm does not need to provide security (collateral).

A **short-term loan** is a sum of money provided to a firm or an individual for a specific, agreed purpose. Repayment of the loan will usually take place within 2 years. Benefits of a bank loan are:
- Bank loans are usually at a fixed rate of interest, making budgeting easier.
- The rate of interest charged is usually lower than the overdraft rate.
- A bank loan may be set up for a long period of time, if needed.

**Factoring** (debt factoring) occurs when a factoring company (usually a bank) buys the right to collect the money from the credit sales of an organisation. Benefits of factoring are:
- Cash flow improves as customer payments (minus a discount) go to the firm.
- There are lower administration costs as the factoring company collects the debts.
- There is a reduced risk of bad debts — the factoring company takes this risk.

**Sale of assets** can improve cash flow by converting an asset, such as property or machinery, into cash which can then be used to ease the cash-flow problem. Benefits of selling assets are:
- Sale of fixed assets can raise a considerable sum of money.
- It is possible that a particular asset is no longer helping towards the business's overall success.

**Sale and leaseback** can improve cash flow by converting an asset, such as property or machinery, into cash. However, the firm is still able to rent or lease the asset. Benefits of sale and leaseback are:
- It provides an immediate inflow of cash.
- A firm can be more flexible as new and more efficient assets can be leased.
- Firms may lease assets such as machinery and computer software so that the owners are responsible for servicing and solving any problems.

## Questions

### Read the following passage and answer the questions that follow.

Jenny was worried about her business's cash flow: a year ago the business had £50,000 in savings; next year she was estimating that her closing balance would be minus £10,000.

It had all started to go wrong when her regular supplier got into financial difficulties and insisted on cash payment on delivery, rather than the 3 months' credit that he had previously given Jenny.

The situation was worsened by the opening of two new competitors, one of them being part of a large chain that gave 6 months' interest-free credit to its customers. Jenny had been slow to react to this new competition, relying on the loyalty of the customer base that she had built up over the last 10 years.

Sales of her products were very seasonal and the competition had opened up in the summer — her peak selling season. Over half of her annual sales revenue occurred in June, July and August.

Jenny had been rather complacent, as she had a healthy bank balance at the time. However, when she sat down to analyse the summer sales in September she realised that, although her bank balance appeared to be good, it was much lower than the balance that she had had the previous September.

Throughout the remainder of the financial year her cash flow steadily declined. Unfortunately, the new competition had coincided with Jenny building a major extension to the store that she owned. She had also spent a lot of money on extra fixtures and fittings and stock, much of which was still in the stockroom.

1 What is meant by the term 'cash flow'?

..................................................................................................................................

..................................................................................................................................

..................................................................................................................................

..................................................................................................................................

**2** Evaluate the main causes of Jenny's cash-flow problems.

**3** Discuss the different ways in which Jenny can overcome her cash-flow problems.

**4** Given the circumstances, was it inevitable that Jenny would suffer from cash-flow problems?

# Measuring and increasing profit

**Profit** is the difference between the income of a business and its total costs (profit = revenue – total costs). **Profitability** is the ability of a business to generate profit or the efficiency of a business in generating profit.

## Measuring profitability

Two ways to measure profitability are the net profit margin and return on capital.

**Net profit margin** measures how well a business is converting its sales revenue into profit.

The net profit margin is calculated as follows:

$$\text{net profit margin (\%)} = \frac{\text{net profit before tax}}{\text{sales (turnover)}} \times 100$$

**Example calculation.** A business makes £11,432 profit from sales revenue of £138,765.

$$\text{net profit margin (\%)} = \frac{£11,432}{£139,450} \times 100 = 8.2\,\%$$

To make sense of this calculation, a firm will usually make use of two comparisons:
- **Comparison over time.** Is 8.2% higher than last year's net profit margin? Over the last 5 years, has the figure generally improved or worsened?
- **Comparison with competitors.** Is 8.2% higher than its main competitors? In recent years, has the business recorded a higher profit margin than its rivals?

**Return on capital** measures how effective a business (or project) is at creating profit from a sum of money invested in the business. It is calculated as follows:

$$\text{return on capital (invested) (\%)} = \frac{\text{net profit before tax}}{\text{capital invested}} \times 100$$

**Example calculation.** A businessman invests £94,500 into opening a new store, which earns a profit of £10,875.

$$\text{return on capital (\%)} = \frac{£10,875}{£94,500} \times 100 = 11.5\,\%$$

For this calculation, a business will also usually make use of two comparisons:
- **Comparison over time.** Is 11.5% higher than the most recent investment?
- **Comparison with alternative investments.** Is 11.5% higher than the business could have earned from alternative investments, such as a different project, an investment in a different business or just keeping the money in an interest-bearing bank account?

## Methods of improving profitability

There are many ways of increasing profit. However, the three most basic methods are:
- **Increasing the price.** If a business increases the price of a product, it will widen the profit margin and therefore each product sold will generate more profit.

- **Decreasing costs.** If the firm can cut its costs, the profit margin will increase. This means that each product will yield more profit.
- **Increasing sales volume.** If costs and price remain the same, it is still possible to increase profits by increasing the volume of products sold.

# The distinction between cash and profit

Profit is calculated by subtracting expenditure from revenue. However, profitable firms may be short of cash for the following reasons:

- If the firm has high stock levels, its wealth will lie in assets rather than cash.
- If the firm's sales are on credit, it will be waiting to receive cash.
- Paying dividends to shareholders will leave a firm short of cash.
- Purchasing fixed assets will involve a large outflow of cash.

## Questions

**Read the following passage and answer the questions that follow.**

Lev's business had been a success to date. His gift shop had increased in profit, although profitability had fallen. Within 5 years he had opened four stores and was planning to add a new range of Russian gifts. He had tested the Russian gifts in his store in Ramsgate and had just printed off the results of the first year of selling this new range. The results are shown in the table.

*Financial data relating to Ramsgate store, 2008*

|  | Usual stock (£) | Russian gifts (£) | Total stock (£) |
|---|---|---|---|
| Sales revenue | 140,000 | 90,000 | 230,000 |
| Profit | 17,000 | 18,000 | 35,000 |
| Net profit margin (%) |  |  |  |

Lev was pleased with these figures, but he was worried that the Russian gifts might have affected the profitability of his usual stock of gifts. In 2008 the Ramsgate store had made a net profit margin of 13% without the Russian gifts and he wanted to be sure that the Russian gifts were not damaging his overall profitability.

Lev had experienced a major cash-flow problem when he had first ordered the Russian gifts. The supplier had insisted on payment on order and it had taken 4 weeks for the gifts to be delivered. Furthermore, they had arrived in early January, missing the Christmas peak, and had therefore stayed on the shelves for longer than Lev would have wished. Lev was forced to offer credit to customers in order to persuade them to buy this new range. However, this problem had only been temporary, as the products became very popular once Lev had organised a major marketing campaign.

After the marketing campaign, Lev kept running out of stock, despite putting up his prices significantly. However, he did run into difficulties with one range of gifts that he had bought cheaply from a new supplier. These had sold well at first, but many of them were returned by customers complaining of substandard quality.

Lev was now considering an investment of £300,000 in order to extend his other shops to stock the Russian gifts. He estimated that he would make a profit of £36,000 in the first year. The money would come from his bank account, where it earned 6% interest. However, a friend was hoping to start a brand new business and was hoping to persuade Lev to put his £300,000 into that business. His friend could make no guarantees but had predicted a 15% return on Lev's capital.

Lev's own business had been based on high-quality gifts selling at high profit margins. He was wondering if this was still the best way to increase his profits.

1 Complete the bottom row of the table, showing the net profit margins.

2 Based on information in the passage, analyse two different factors that might have led to Lev being short of cash, despite having a profitable business.

3 Evaluate whether Lev should keep his £300,000 in the bank, invest it in his friend's new business, or invest it into extending his other shops to stock the Russian gifts.

4 Lev is considering three other ways of increasing his profit:
- reducing costs
- increasing prices
- increasing sales volume

Discuss the relative merits of these three strategies.

........................................................................................................................................................

........................................................................................................................................................

........................................................................................................................................................

........................................................................................................................................................

........................................................................................................................................................

........................................................................................................................................................

........................................................................................................................................................

........................................................................................................................................................

........................................................................................................................................................

........................................................................................................................................................

........................................................................................................................................................

# Improving organisational structures

# Organisational structure and levels of hierarchy

The following key terms are important:

- **Organisational structure** is the relationship between different people and functions within an organisation.
- An **organisation chart** is a diagram showing the lines of authority and layers of hierarchy in an organisation.
- **Organisational hierarchy** is the vertical division of authority and accountability in an organisation.
- **Levels of hierarchy** are the number of different supervisory and management levels between the shop-floor and the chief executive within an organisation.
- The **span of control** is the number of subordinates whom a manager is required to supervise directly.

## Tall structures with narrow spans of control

These structures have the following features:

- They offer more promotional opportunities because the career ladder has more rungs on it.
- More layers mean more staff, which in turn means higher company overheads.
- There is less delegation, which could lead to low morale and lack of commitment.
- There is tight control, which might be beneficial if factors such as quality, safety or security are crucial, and if mistakes may have very serious consequences.
- Important information may be lost in reporting up through the many levels of the hierarchy.
- With a longer chain of command it takes longer for decisions to be made.

## Flat structures with wide spans of control

These structures have the following features:

- Individual managers have less time for each subordinate and must delegate.
- More delegation means greater responsibility, but this may lead to stress.
- Vertical communication improves.
- Reduced overhead costs should mean greater efficiency within the organisation.

## Workforce roles, workloads and job allocation

Workloads are determined by the nature of the organisation and the management structure. A large span of control or a lack of delegation can increase workloads. A change in the organisational structure can change job allocations. Work roles generally involve directors, managers, supervisors and/or team leaders and operatives.

The structure of an organisation is influenced by many factors including: the size of the organisation; the nature of the organisation; the culture and attitudes of senior management; and the skill and experience of its workforce.

## Questions

1 What is the purpose of an organisation chart?

2 Define the terms 'levels of hierarchy' and 'span of control' in relation to an organisation's structure, and explain the relationship between them.

3 Consider the advantages and disadvantages for a business of having a tall hierarchical organisational structure with a narrow span of control.

4 In some organisations, there is a narrow span of control at senior levels of management, but wider spans of control at shop-floor supervisor level. Consider why this is likely to be the case and whether there is an ideal span of control.

**5** How might workloads and job allocations in any organisation be influenced by organisational structures?

**6** Analyse the factors that might influence the structure of any organisation.

**7** Traditionally, organisations have tended to have very tall hierarchical structures, but more recently, hierarchies have become flatter. Assess the implications for business of this development.

# Delegation

The following key terms are important:
- **Delegation** is the process of passing authority from a manager to a subordinate.
- **Responsibility** means being accountable for one's actions.
- **Authority** is the ability or power to carry out a task.
- **Accountability** is the extent to which a named individual is held responsible for the success or failure of a particular policy, project or piece of work.

In delegation, the subordinate is given the authority to make decisions connected with a particular task, but the manager remains accountable for decisions taken.

## Effective delegation

The following factors are likely to improve the effectiveness of delegation:
- Delegation must be based on mutual trust between manager and subordinate.
- It is important to delegate to the most suitable person.
- Interesting and challenging tasks should be delegated as well as routine ones.
- The tasks and responsibilities to be delegated must be clearly explained.
- As well as delegating responsibility, managers must also delegate the authority.
- The limitations of the subordinate's authority should be made clear.
- Managers must relinquish control so that subordinates feel they are trusted.

## Advantages and limitations

Advantages of delegation include:
- There is a limit to the amount of work that managers can carry out themselves.
- Delegation empowers and motivates workers.
- Subordinates may have better local knowledge, which may improve decisions.
- Delegation may allow greater flexibility and a quicker response to changes.
- Delegation is an effective form of management development.

Limits to delegation include:
- In some small firms, owner-managers are reluctant to relinquish control.
- Customers may want to see the manager, even though responsibilities have been delegated.
- The leadership style in an organisation will largely dictate the extent to which responsibilities are delegated down the hierarchy.
- The extent to which responsibilities can be delegated is influenced by the skills of staff.
- In emergency or crisis situations where decisions need to be made quickly, or where there is a need for confidentiality or extreme security, less delegation is likely to take place and it is often less effective.

## Questions

**Read the following passage and answer the questions that follow.**

> Mena Potts is the finance manager at Trentham Tables Ltd. Her new assistant, Jake Newton, is relatively inexperienced but keen to learn and to take responsibility. Mena will be away for a week and will be leaving Jake in charge. She has delegated to him responsibility for paying invoices and for making a range of decisions. She has given him the authority to sign cheques. Invoices are rarely for more than £1,000 and because she is ultimately accountable, she has set a limit of £1,000 on the cheques that Jake can sign. She has informed other colleagues of the authority she has given to Jake and the responsibility he has for taking decisions in her absence.

1 Define the term 'delegation'.

2 Using the example above, distinguish between the terms 'responsibility', 'authority' and 'accountability'.

3 Passing on authority is an issue that many managers find difficult. Using the example above, why, if insufficient authority is transferred, is delegation likely to be unsuccessful?

4 Why might Jake be keen for Mena to delegate more tasks to him?

**5** Consider the factors that are likely to make delegation more effective.

......................................................................................................................................

......................................................................................................................................

......................................................................................................................................

......................................................................................................................................

**6** Consider the limitations to effective delegation in business.

......................................................................................................................................

......................................................................................................................................

......................................................................................................................................

......................................................................................................................................

**7** How important is effective delegation to an organisation's success?

......................................................................................................................................

......................................................................................................................................

......................................................................................................................................

......................................................................................................................................

# Communication flows

## The process of communication

**Communication** is the process of exchanging information or ideas between two or more individuals or groups. **Internal communication** is the exchange of information between people within an organisation. **External communication** is the exchange of information with individuals, groups and organisations outside the business.

The process of communication involves the following features:
- a sender or communicator — the person or group sending the message
- the message — the topic of the communication
- a transmission mechanism by which a message is conveyed
- a receiver — the person or group whom the message is aimed at
- feedback — the response from the receiver

**One-way communication** is communication without any feedback, while **two-way communication** involves an opportunity to give feedback.

# Communication channels

A **communication channel** is the route through which communication occurs. **Open channels** of communication are where any staff member can see, read or hear the discussions and conclusions. **Closed channels** of communication are where access to information is restricted. **Formal channels** of communication are those established and approved by senior management. **Informal channels** of communication involve passing information outside the official/formal channels, using 'the grapevine' and gossip. **Vertical communication** is when information is passed up and down the chain of command. **Lateral communication** is when people at the same level in an organisation pass information to each other.

# Effective communication

Effective communication offers organisations a number of benefits:
- It enables the business to make more informed decisions based on better-quality information.
- It is easier to implement change.
- Effective communication encourages a more motivated and committed workforce.
- It helps to ensure good coordination and the pursuit of corporate objectives.
- It allows the organisation to be more competitive.

# Links between organisational structure and business performance

Organisational hierarchies, spans of control, the clarity of lines of accountability and the quality of delegation all affect business performance.

Organisational structure influences the effectiveness of communication, which influences the quality of decision making, how easy it is to introduce change, the motivation of workers and the extent to which the business is in tune with its customers — all of which influence efficiency and competitiveness.

## Questions

1 Outline the benefits to a firm of good communication and the problems that a firm might encounter if it has poor communication.

........................................................................................

........................................................................................

........................................................................................

........................................................................................

........................................................................................

2 Distinguish between:

a internal and external communication

b one-way and two-way communication

3 Explain the process of communication and the elements involved.

4 Which two of the following statements are true?

A Formal communication means written communication.

B Written communication can be either formal or informal communication.

C Informal communication means oral communication.

D Oral communication can be either formal or informal communication.

5 Why is the informal communication that takes place within a business so important?

6 Discuss the extent to which upward vertical communication can aid decision making and thus benefit an organisation.

_____

_____

_____

_____

_____

_____

_____

_____

_____

7 To what extent might organisational structure affect business performance?

_____

_____

_____

_____

_____

_____

_____

_____

_____

_____

# Measuring the effectiveness of the workforce

## Labour productivity

**Labour productivity** is a measure of the output per worker in a given time period. The formula is:

$$\text{labour productivity} = \frac{\text{output per period}}{\text{number of employees per period}}$$

An increase in labour productivity means that output will be increased using the same number of employees. An increase in labour productivity also implies a lower labour cost per unit (assuming wages stay the same), which will enable the business to charge a lower price and/or gain a higher profit margin.

## Labour turnover

**Labour turnover** is the proportion of employees leaving a business over a given time period. The formula is:

$$\text{labour turnover} = \frac{\text{number leaving a business over a given period}}{\text{average number employed over a given period}} \times 100$$

Labour turnover can be caused by both internal and external factors. Internal factors include unchallenging jobs and poor communication. An external factor might be an increase in vacancies for more attractive jobs in other firms.

Problems caused by high labour turnover include:
- high recruitment and selection costs
- high induction and training costs
- in some industries, a need to redesign jobs to keep them as simple as possible
- reduced productivity
- low morale among existing workers

Labour turnover can be improved by:
- monitoring trends and identifying problem areas
- exit interviews
- effective recruitment and selection procedures
- high-quality induction and training
- career development

## Absenteeism

The **rate of absenteeism** is the proportion of employees not at work on a given day. The formula is:

$$\text{rate of absenteeism} = \frac{\text{number of staff absent on 1 day}}{\text{total number of staff}} \times 100$$

The formula for calculating the absentee rate for a year is:

$$\text{annual rate of absenteeism} = \frac{\text{total number of days lost due to absence during the year}}{\text{total number of days that could be worked} \times \text{number of staff}} \times 100$$

Problems arising from absenteeism, such as increased costs, delays in production and reduced productivity and quality, may lead to dissatisfied customers and reduced profits.

Strategies to reduce absenteeism include:
- introducing more flexible working practices
- ensuring jobs are interesting and challenging
- improving working conditions
- improving relations between employers and employees
- introducing attendance bonuses
- monitoring trends and identifying problem areas

# Health and safety

The formula for calculating the rate of absenteeism due to health and safety is:

$$\frac{\text{rate of absenteeism}}{\text{due to health and safety}} = \frac{\text{number of working days lost per year for health and safety reasons}}{\text{total number of possible working days per year}} \times 100$$

## Questions

**Read the following and answer the questions that follow.**

The human resources department of Agra Engineering Ltd has the following personnel data.

| | **2005** | **2006** | **2007** |
|---|---|---|---|
| Total output (units) | 12,600 | 13,500 | 14,960 |
| Average number of employees | 200 | 180 | 170 |
| Number of employees leaving | 15 | 20 | 25 |
| Number of working days | 250 | 250 | 250 |
| Total number of days lost due to absence | 1,200 | 1,440 | 1,700 |
| Total number of days lost due to health and safety reasons | 30 | 20 | 15 |

| | Marketing | | | Production | | | Administration | | | Finance | | |
|---|---|---|---|---|---|---|---|---|---|---|---|---|
| | 2005 | 2006 | 2007 | 2005 | 2006 | 2007 | 2005 | 2006 | 2007 | 2005 | 2006 | 2007 |
| Employees | 20 | 20 | 20 | 162 | 142 | 132 | 10 | 10 | 10 | 8 | 8 | 8 |
| Leavers | 1 | 1 | 2 | 13 | 11 | 13 | 0 | 8 | 9 | 1 | 0 | 1 |
| Absences (days) | 85 | 85 | 70 | 425 | 460 | 580 | 50 | 95 | 90 | 40 | 80 | 110 |
| Health and safety absences (days) | 1 | 2 | 0 | 28 | 17 | 15 | 1 | 0 | 0 | 0 | 1 | 0 |

**1** Explain the term 'labour productivity' and outline three ways in which a firm might increase its labour productivity.

.......................................................................................................................................................................

.......................................................................................................................................................................

.......................................................................................................................................................................

.......................................................................................................................................................................

.......................................................................................................................................................................

**2** Define the term 'labour turnover' and explain two problems that high rates of labour turnover might cause a firm.

.......................................................................................................................................................................

.......................................................................................................................................................................

.......................................................................................................................................................................

.......................................................................................................................................................................

.......................................................................................................................................................................

**3** Analyse why labour turnover is higher in an industry such as hotels and catering than in many other industries.

.......................................................................................................................................................................

.......................................................................................................................................................................

.......................................................................................................................................................................

.......................................................................................................................................................................

.......................................................................................................................................................................

4 Outline two possible causes of a high rate of absenteeism for any firm and two consequences of a high rate of absenteeism.

5 For each of the 3 years for which there are data, calculate Agra Engineering's:

a labour productivity

b rate of labour turnover

c annual absence rate

d health and safety absentee rate

6 Explain how the above four measures of workforce effectiveness might be an indication of how well a human resource management programme is operating.

7 Discuss the issues that the personnel data available for Agra Engineering Ltd raise for the firm's human resource management policies.

...........................................................................................................................................................

...........................................................................................................................................................

...........................................................................................................................................................

...........................................................................................................................................................

...........................................................................................................................................................

...........................................................................................................................................................

...........................................................................................................................................................

...........................................................................................................................................................

...........................................................................................................................................................

# Developing an effective workforce: recruitment, selection and training

# Recruitment and selection

## The recruitment process

**Recruitment** involves identifying the need for new employees, attracting the 'best' candidates for the job and selecting the most suitable candidate. The process involves the following stages:

- workforce planning
- job analysis resulting in job descriptions
- production of person (job) specifications
- decisions on whether to use internal or external recruitment
- decisions on the most appropriate advertising media to use to attract candidates
- decisions on whether applicants need to submit application forms or CVs
- short-listing the best applicants
- interviews and other methods of assessment to select the best candidate
- appointing the candidate, taking into account equal opportunities legislation

## Effective recruitment and selection

Methods of recruitment and selection depend on a number of factors, including:

- the level of the job within the firm, whether shop-floor or senior management
- the size of the organisation, whether a large multinational or a small shop
- the resources available to fund the recruitment and selection process
- the cost of any particular method
- the supply of potential applicants with relevant skills and experience
- cultural factors (e.g. whether internal recruitment and promotion is the norm)

Ineffective selection can cause increased labour turnover, which in turn leads to additional costs in terms of further advertising, interviewing and training as well as having a negative impact on productivity and employee motivation.

## Questions

1 How can workforce planning assist in the recruitment and selection process?

2 Identify the type of characteristics that should be included in a person specification and explain how a person specification differs from a job description.

*(Continued overleaf)*

**3** Discuss the benefits and the problems that a business such as ASDA might face if it recruits the majority of its senior management from within the business.

**4** Identify the method of advertising that would be most suitable for each of the following jobs:

**a** a sales assistant in a local corner shop

**b** a headteacher in a large local secondary school

**c** an army cadet

**d** a graduate trainee for Marks and Spencer

**5** Explain one advantage of an application form over a CV and one advantage of a CV over an application form.

6 Identify two methods of selection other than interview and consider how effective interviews are in comparison to these other methods.

........................................................................................................................................

........................................................................................................................................

........................................................................................................................................

........................................................................................................................................

........................................................................................................................................

7 Identify five areas of equal opportunities legislation that need to be taken into account when selecting the best person for a job.

........................................................................................................................................

........................................................................................................................................

........................................................................................................................................

........................................................................................................................................

........................................................................................................................................

8 Consider how effective recruitment and selection processes contribute to the success of a business.

........................................................................................................................................

........................................................................................................................................

........................................................................................................................................

........................................................................................................................................

9 Discuss the factors that determine the most effective methods of recruitment and selection for an organisation.

........................................................................................................................................

........................................................................................................................................

........................................................................................................................................

........................................................................................................................................

........................................................................................................................................

........................................................................................................................................

........................................................................................................................................

........................................................................................................................................

# Training

**Training** is the provision of work-related education, either on-the-job or off-the-job, involving employees being taught new skills or improving existing skills. **Training needs** arise when the knowledge and skills required exceed or differ from those that workers currently possess.

## Benefits of training

Training offers businesses the following benefits:
- It helps new employees reach the levels of performance of experienced workers.
- It develops a knowledgeable and committed workforce.
- It increases efficiency and productivity.
- It identifies employees' potential.
- It reduces costs (reduced accidents and wastage) and increases productivity.
- It encourages employees to deal with change more effectively.
- It encourages employees to work towards the organisation's goals.
- It improves the image of the company.

## Induction training

**Induction training** is for new employees and usually involves learning about the way the business works rather than about the particular job that the individual will do. Its aim is to help new employees settle in quickly, in order to ensure that they reach the level of performance expected of experienced workers as soon as possible.

## External and internal training

**External training**, such as joining a college course, is appropriate if there are only a few employees with a specific training need and if their training requirements are not linked specifically to the organisation.

**Internal training** can be used if training needs are specific to the organisation — for example, if employees need to learn how to use a particular new computer system.

## On-the-job and off-the-job training

**On-the-job training** is where an employee learns a job by seeing how it is carried out by an experienced employee. **Off-the-job training** includes all forms of employee education apart from that provided at the immediate workplace.

On-the-job training is cheaper than off-the-job training and takes place in a realistic working environment with no significant loss of output. However, the quality of training depends on the ability of the instructor and whether the work situation is a suitable place for training. Off-the-job training focuses more on generic skills and knowledge, uses experts to do the teaching and enables employees to meet staff from other organisations.

# How to evaluate training

The outcomes of some training can be more easily observed than others. For example, training in the use of a new piece of computer software is easier to monitor than a management training course. In the latter case, questionnaires may be used to assess views and perceptions. Mystery visitors may be used to check on how staff respond to customers. Other methods include monitoring improvements in the quality of output, reductions in labour turnover, increases in internal promotions and reductions in accidents and wastage.

## Questions

1 If training is a response to changes, explain two changes that might cause a firm to introduce a new training programme.

2 Identify six benefits to a firm of effective training.

3 Explain how induction training differs from general training and outline the benefits to a firm of providing an effective induction training programme.

**4** What is the difference between internal and external training?

_____

_____

_____

_____

**5** Discuss the relative merits of on-the-job training and off-the-job training for a business that is trying to develop and introduce new technology into its processes.

_____

_____

_____

_____

_____

_____

_____

_____

**6** As a human resource manager, discuss how you might attempt to evaluate the effectiveness of the training programmes within your firm.

_____

_____

_____

_____

_____

_____

_____

_____

_____

7 Discuss the differences between the types of training that would be most appropriate for developing the effectiveness of a sales assistant in a store such as Top Shop and a regional manager for Top Shop.

.................................................................................................................................................................

.................................................................................................................................................................

.................................................................................................................................................................

.................................................................................................................................................................

.................................................................................................................................................................

.................................................................................................................................................................

.................................................................................................................................................................

.................................................................................................................................................................

.................................................................................................................................................................

.................................................................................................................................................................

8 To what extent should the provision of training be a response to current problems faced by a firm or the well-thought-out plans for its future knowledge and skills requirements?

.................................................................................................................................................................

.................................................................................................................................................................

.................................................................................................................................................................

.................................................................................................................................................................

.................................................................................................................................................................

.................................................................................................................................................................

.................................................................................................................................................................

.................................................................................................................................................................

.................................................................................................................................................................

.................................................................................................................................................................

# Theories of motivation

## Scientific management and F. W. Taylor

Taylor believed that extreme division of labour, payment by piecework and tight management control were the main methods of improving productivity and efficiency. However, his influence on the workforce was less successful because extreme division of labour meant that jobs became more boring and repetitive, and the lack of skills needed by workers led to a loss of power for individual workers.

## The human relations school and Elton Mayo

Mayo's findings suggested that:
- Recognition, belonging and security are important motivators.
- Work is a group-based activity.
- Managers need to pay attention to individuals' social needs and the influence of their informal groups.
- Managers must communicate with informal groups and involve them in decision making to ensure their goals are in tune with the organisation's goals.
- Improved communication can lead to increased output.

## Maslow's hierarchy of human needs

Maslow's hierarchy of needs suggests that people have similar types of need, which can be classified into a hierarchy. He believed that an unsatisfied need was a motivator of behaviour and that, while it remained unsatisfied, higher-level needs were unimportant. However, once people satisfy their physiological and safety needs, it is questionable whether, for all individuals, social needs come before esteem needs. Many individuals are high achievers and are motivated by this, sometimes to the exclusion of any desire to be part of a team or to get along with their colleagues.

## Herzberg's motivation and maintenance

Herzberg developed the two-factor theory of job satisfaction and dissatisfaction. He called the factors that motivate and give job satisfaction **motivators**. Factors that can reduce job dissatisfaction are called **hygiene factors** or **maintenance factors**. Ensuring that the latter are acceptable to the workforce prevents dissatisfaction rather than causing positive motivation. Herzberg also distinguished between **movement** (when someone does something for a specific purpose or because they have to) and **motivation** (when someone wants to do something for its own sake) and suggested that reward-based systems, such as bonuses, would provide only short-term motivation or 'movement'. One of the main policy recommendations that stemmed from Herzberg's work is **job enrichment**.

## Questions

1 Explain what is meant by F. W. Taylor's scientific management school of thought and what the impact of this approach on employees' motivation is likely to be.

.................................................................................................................................................

.................................................................................................................................................

.................................................................................................................................................

.................................................................................................................................................

.................................................................................................................................................

.................................................................................................................................................

2 Outline Elton Mayo's human relations school of management and explain how this differs from the scientific school of management.

.................................................................................................................................................

.................................................................................................................................................

.................................................................................................................................................

.................................................................................................................................................

.................................................................................................................................................

3 Sketch Maslow's hierarchy of human needs and explain the various levels and their relevance to a work context.

4 Identify four of Herzberg's motivators and four of Herzberg's maintenance or hygiene factors.

..............................................................................................................................

..............................................................................................................................

..............................................................................................................................

..............................................................................................................................

..............................................................................................................................

5 Distinguish between the effect of Herzberg's motivators and that of his maintenance or hygiene factors on the motivation of employees.

..............................................................................................................................

..............................................................................................................................

..............................................................................................................................

..............................................................................................................................

6 Analyse the links between Maslow's hierarchy of human needs and Herzberg's two-factor theory.

..............................................................................................................................

..............................................................................................................................

..............................................................................................................................

..............................................................................................................................

..............................................................................................................................

..............................................................................................................................

7 To what extent can the theories of motivation be applied effectively to work situations in business today?

..............................................................................................................................

..............................................................................................................................

..............................................................................................................................

..............................................................................................................................

..............................................................................................................................

..............................................................................................................................

..............................................................................................................................

# Using financial methods to motivate employees

## Financial motivators

Businesses use several financial payment systems to motivate employees.

- **Time rates.** These include salary and wage systems where payment is for input rather than output.
- **Piecework.** In this system, payment is based on the number of items produced. It can provide an incentive to work hard. However, it may cause staff to concentrate on quantity rather than quality; output may be influenced by workers' needs rather than customer demand; it may increase resistance to change; and it may cause movement rather than motivation.
- **Performance-related pay (PRP).** A bonus or salary increase is awarded for above average performance. Decisions on PRP usually take place following an appraisal that assesses performance.

  *Advantages:* it makes a direct link between pay and effort; it reduces costs, increases productivity and improves quality; motivation improves and labour turnover and absenteeism are reduced; individual targets are linked to corporate objectives.

  *Disadvantages:* it can cause conflict among staff receiving different bonuses but doing the same job; its effect on motivation may be negligible; it is often introduced into jobs where it is difficult to measure performance; there is a reduction in collective bargaining as pay decisions are related to individuals.

- **Profit sharing.** A proportion of a firm's profit is divided among its employees in the form of a bonus paid in addition to an employee's salary.

  *Advantages:* it reduces employees' 'them and us' feelings; it reduces resistance to change; it provides incentives to keep costs down and productivity up in order to improve profits.

  *Problems:* it has little effect on motivation; it can cause free-rider problems; there may be uncertainty in financial planning if employees come to depend on bonuses; large payouts from profits may affect both shareholder dividends and profit retained for investment, with adverse consequences for the firm.

- **Share ownership and share options.** Shares may be given to employees or sold to them at favourable rates. This encourages employees to identify with company objectives, recognising that their rewards (share value and dividends) are dependent on company performance. Under share options, individuals are given the option of buying a fixed number of shares at a fixed price, by a given date. Share options provide senior management with the incentive to perform at their very best. However, they may lead to short-termism and can lead to excessive financial rewards in the boardroom.

- **Fringe benefits.** These are rewards given to employees without increasing wages or salaries. They add to costs but pay for themselves by, for example, encouraging staff loyalty and reducing labour turnover.

# Money as a motivator

Financial incentives are used:

- to overcome or reduce resistance to change
- where managers see money as a major means of control
- when firms are looking to meet short-term goals

However, despite their widespread use and short-term benefits, most evidence suggests that money is not a major motivator in the long term.

## Questions

1 What are 'time rates' and why are they used to pay sales assistants and clerical workers?

2 Explain the term 'piece rates' (piecework) and outline two problems a business might encounter as a result of using piece rates to pay its employees.

3 What does the term 'performance-related pay' (PRP) mean? Explain two advantages and two disadvantages to a business of using PRP.

4 Explain one advantage and one disadvantage to a business of using a system of profit sharing to reward employees.

5 Explain one advantage and one disadvantage to a business of using share ownership as a means of providing financial incentives for employees.

6 Explain, using an example, what a share option is.

7 List three examples of fringe benefits that a business might offer its employees.

8 To what extent is it easier to motivate workers with financial incentives in the short term than in the longer term?

*(Continued overleaf)*

# Non-financial methods of motivating employees

Businesses can improve employee motivation by improving job design. This can de done by:

- **Job enlargement.** This involves increasing the scope of a job, either by job enrichment or by job rotation.
- **Job enrichment** is where the job is expanded vertically by giving the worker more responsibility.
  *Advantages:* it relieves boredom; it ensures that there is cover for staff who are absent; it improves motivation; it encourages greater participation in the production process.
  *Problems:* some may find the process intimidating and feel that it places unwanted pressure on them; by delegating responsibility, it could be viewed as an attempt to get more out of workers while paying them the same rate; it may be costly and benefits may only result in the long term; not all jobs lend themselves to enrichment.
- **Job rotation** is where the job is expanded horizontally by giving the worker more tasks, but at the same level of responsibility.
  *Advantages:* it develops workers' unused skills and presents them with challenges; it allows workers to make greater contributions to the decision-making process; it enhances workers' promotional prospects; it motivates workers.
  *Problems:* training costs increase and output may fall because of less specialisation; it may be seen as simply a greater number of boring tasks.
- **Empowering employees.** Empowerment means giving employees the means by which they can exercise power over their working lives. It involves: recognising that workers are capable of doing more; making workers feel trusted and confident to carry out jobs and make decisions without supervision; recognising workers' achievements; creating an environment where workers wish to contribute and to be involved.
- **Working in teams.** Teamworking is a system where a group of employees work together to meet shared objectives. For example, a team of people producing a complete car will need to be multi-skilled, well trained and motivated by more than the piece-rate rewards received by workers carrying out a single, repetitive task. By using teamworking, an organisation gets a more motivated, flexible workforce that can cover absences more easily. When accompanied by other techniques, teamwork can enhance motivation.

# Links between organisational structure and the motivational techniques

Motivational techniques and organisational structure are linked by the following concepts:
- levels of hierarchy and spans of control
- lines of accountability
- delegation and empowerment
- communication
- flexible working

## Questions

1 Explain three problems for a business that might result from a low level of motivation among its employees.

2 Distinguish between the terms 'job enlargement', 'job enrichment' and 'job rotation'.

3 Explain two advantages and two disadvantages to a business of introducing job enrichment.

4 Outline how job enrichment is linked to two motivation theories with which you are familiar.

5 Explain one advantage and one disadvantage to a business of introducing a system of job rotation.

6 What does the term 'empowerment' mean?

7 Consider how the introduction of teamworking and the empowering of employees might benefit a business.

8 Analyse the links between a firm's organisational structure and the motivational techniques available to its management.

9 To what extent might effective communication and feedback improve employee motivation and a
firm's performance?

# Making operational decisions

**Operations management** is the process that uses the resources of an organisation to provide the right goods or services for the customer.

**Operational targets** are the goals or aims of the operations function of the business. Three examples of operational targets will be considered:
- unit costs
- measures of quality
- capacity utilisation

## Unit costs

Unit cost is the cost of producing 1 unit of output. It is calculated by the following formula:

$$\text{unit cost} = \frac{\text{total cost}}{\text{units of output}}$$

The unit cost is also known as the average cost (AC) or average total cost (ATC). For example, if a business produces 3,000 units of output at a total cost of £75,000, the average (or unit) cost is £75,000/3,000 = £25.

## Measures of quality

Some commonly used measures of quality are as follows:
- **Customer satisfaction ratings.** A survey can reveal customer opinions on a numerical scale.
- **Customer complaints.** This calculates the number of customers who complain as a percentage of the total number.
- **Scrap rate (%).** This calculates the percentage of items rejected during production.
- **Punctuality.** This calculates the degree to which a business delivers its products (or provides its services) on time. It is often measured as a percentage:

$$\text{punctuality (\%)} = \frac{\text{deliveries on time}}{\text{total deliveries}} \times 100$$

## Capacity utilisation

**Capacity** is the maximum total level of output that a business can produce in a given time period. A company producing at this level is said to be producing at full capacity.

**Capacity utilisation** is the percentage of a firm's total possible production level that is being reached.

**Under-utilisation of capacity** is when a firm's output is below the maximum possible. This is also known as **excess capacity** or **spare capacity**.

**Capacity shortage** occurs when a firm's capacity is not large enough to meet demands. Capacity utilisation can be calculated using the following formula:

$$\text{capacity utilisation (\%)} = \frac{\text{actual output per annum (month)}}{\text{maximum possible output per annum (month)}} \times 100$$

Spare capacity (or under-utilisation of capacity) can be caused by:
- falling demand, perhaps caused by new competitors
- unsuccessful marketing
- seasonal demand
- over-investment in fixed assets — too much capacity

However, spare capacity does have some advantages:
- There is more time for maintenance and repair of machinery.
- There may be less pressure and stress for employees.
- A firm can cope with a sudden increase in demand.

## Matching production and demand

In order to maximise its efficiency, a business will try to achieve full capacity utilisation. This can be achieved by balancing demand and supply of products.
- **Demand.** If a business has spare capacity, it can attempt to improve its marketing in order to increase demand.
- **Supply.** If a business has spare capacity, it might decide to follow a policy of rationalisation in order to reduce its capacity and save unnecessary expenditure.

**Rationalisation** is a process by which a firm improves its efficiency by cutting the scale of its operations.

A business may reduce its capacity by selling off all or a part of its production area; changing to a shorter working week or shorter day; or laying off workers.

It may increase its capacity by building or extending factories or plants; asking staff to work overtime or longer hours; hiring new staff; or subcontracting.

**Stock control** is another method that can be used to ensure that production matches demand. By holding high stock levels, a business is able to release additional products on to the market when demand increases.

## Dealing with non-standard orders

A **non-standard order** is a business decision relating to a one-off contract. When deciding whether to accept such an order, the key operational factors to consider are:
- Is there sufficient capacity?
- What is the impact on costs?
- Is there potential for future (profitable) orders?
- How will staff morale be affected?

## Questions

**Read the following passage and answer the questions that follow.**

Sheena looked at the data relating to her three factories.

*Data on three factories*

|  | Maximum capacity output | Actual units of output | Capacity utilisation (%) | Total costs (£) | Unit costs (£) |
|---|---|---|---|---|---|
| Factory A | 6,000 | 4,500 |  | 270,000 |  |
| Factory B | 6,000 | 2,700 |  | 216,000 |  |
| Factory C | 8,000 | 4,800 |  | 336,000 |  |
| Total | 20,000 | 12,000 |  | 822,000 |  |

Sheena was struggling. Her main competitor was achieving unit costs of £60 per unit and 95% capacity utilisation.

Sheena was considering closing one of her factories but was hesitating because sales were seasonal and she worked at higher capacity levels in some months. Furthermore, her sales team had developed a new product that had recorded much higher levels of customer satisfaction than those produced by her main competitor, and Sheena was optimistic that this new product would lead to much higher sales.

With low capacity utilisation, Sheena was also able to react quickly to changes in demand and so provide punctual deliveries. Her workforce was also able to spend more time on ensuring that raw materials and finished products were handled carefully so that waste levels were reduced and a high-quality product manufactured. Until recently she had subcontracted some production to her friend Kim, who was still keen to supply her if she wanted extra production.

Another reason for Sheena's hesitation was the fact that Carter Ltd had offered her a special order contract. It was offering her £75 an item if she could deliver 6,000 items. It had initially approached her competitor, who had refused the offer.

Carter Ltd had hinted that this 6,000 order could become an annual order if she supplied a good-quality product, promptly.

**1** State three different measures of quality mentioned in the article.

**2** Explain two ways in which Sheena might increase her capacity, if necessary.

**3** Fill in the gaps in the table by calculating the figures for capacity utilisation and unit costs.

**4** Based on your calculations in question 2, and any other information, evaluate the extent to which Sheena is competing effectively with her main competitor.

**5** Should Sheena accept the special order from Carter Ltd? Justify your view.

# Developing effective operations: quality

**Quality** is defined as those features of a product or service that allow it to satisfy (or delight) customers. Some widely accepted measures of quality are:
- appearance
- reliability
- functions (added extras)
- after-sales service: cost, promptness and effectiveness
- image and reputation
- ethical rating

## Quality systems

A **quality system** is the approach used by an organisation in order to achieve quality. Most quality systems can be classified under two headings: quality control and quality assurance. Having a quality system offers a business several benefits:
- **Impact on sales volume.** If a product or service meets the needs of customers, demand should increase.
- **Creating a unique selling point (USP).** High quality can be used as a unique selling point to increase demand.
- **Impact on selling price.** Having a unique selling point encourages consumers to pay a higher price.
- **Pricing flexibility.** A reputation for quality also gives a firm the ability to be more flexible in its pricing. The money it makes from loyal customers will guarantee a profit, allowing the firm to offer discounted prices in order to attract other customers.
- **Cost reductions.** Quality systems reduce wastage of materials.

However, introducing and managing a quality system involves the following issues:
- **Costs.** The system is expensive to set up, monitor and review.
- **Training the workforce.** This is an essential cost and can involve disruption to production.

## The distinction between quality control and quality assurance

**Quality control** is a system that uses inspection as a way of finding any faults in the good or service being provided. It offers the following benefits:
- Inspection can prevent a defective product reaching the customer.
- It is a more secure system than one that trusts every individual.
- Inspectors may detect common problems throughout an organisation.

**Quality assurance** is a system that aims to achieve or improve quality by organising every process to get the product 'right first time' and prevent mistakes ever happening. Its benefits are:
- Workers are given total responsibility for the product; theorists such as Herzberg argue that this motivates workers.
- Costs are reduced because there is less waste and fewer faulty products.

A widely recognised quality assurance system is **total quality management** (TQM). The strategy aims to eliminate problems by using a 'right first time' approach.

# Quality standards

**Quality standards** are awards that provide some proof that a business provides a quality good or service.

BS 5750 is a British Standards award granted to organisations that possess quality assurance systems that meet the standards set. ISO 9001 is the international standard that is equivalent to BS 5750.

The benefits of these awards are:
- marketing advantages from the acknowledgement of higher quality standards
- greater employee motivation from the sense of responsibility and recognition
- financial benefits in the long term, from the elimination of waste and the improved reputation of the firm

## Questions

**Read the following passage and answer the questions that follow.**

George's business had just completed its 10,000th tractor. Although the business could not match overseas competitors on price, it was thriving because of the reliability of George's tractors, the after-sales service (which guaranteed a temporary replacement within 12 hours of breakdown), the environmental features of the tractors (which used manure as fuel), and the high-tech equipment, such as the automated navigation system which could be programmed to plough a field without the need for a driver.

Originally, George had used a quality control system to ensure the quality of his tractors, but as the tractors became more complex he changed to TQM — a quality assurance system. At first this damaged the company's profitability, but quite quickly it led to some major improvements in quality and savings in costs.

For many years George had been reluctant to use a quality standard system, arguing that it was a 'waste of money'. Eventually he agreed to apply for the ISO 9001 standard. There was a significant increase in sales immediately, involving a rise in both the volume sold and the price of the tractors, although George did not believe that his tractors were any better than they had been before.

1 What is meant by the term 'quality'?

-------------------------------------------------------------------

-------------------------------------------------------------------

**2** Identify three measures of quality mentioned in the passage.

..................................................................................................................................................................

..................................................................................................................................................................

..................................................................................................................................................................

**3** What is meant by the initials 'TQM'?

..................................................................................................................................................................

**4** Briefly analyse why achieving ISO 9001 would help George's business.

..................................................................................................................................................................

..................................................................................................................................................................

..................................................................................................................................................................

..................................................................................................................................................................

..................................................................................................................................................................

..................................................................................................................................................................

**5** Evaluate the reasons why George's decision to change from quality control to quality assurance initially led to a fall in profit but eventually led to an increase in profit.

..................................................................................................................................................................

..................................................................................................................................................................

..................................................................................................................................................................

..................................................................................................................................................................

..................................................................................................................................................................

..................................................................................................................................................................

..................................................................................................................................................................

..................................................................................................................................................................

..................................................................................................................................................................

..................................................................................................................................................................

..................................................................................................................................................................

..................................................................................................................................................................

# Developing effective operations: customer service

**Customer service** is the overall activity of identifying and satisfying customer needs and the delivery of a level of service that meets or exceeds customer expectations.

**Customer expectations** are what people think should happen and how they think they should be treated when asking for or receiving customer service.

## The meaning of customer service: what do customers want?

A survey by the ICS found that the top five customer priorities concerned:
- the overall quality of the product or service supplied
- the friendliness of the staff in dealing with the processing of the good or service
- the efficiency with which problems and complaints were handled
- the speed of service or delivery of the product in comparison to the promises made
- the helpfulness of staff in general

## Methods of meeting customer expectations

Meeting customer expectations can be achieved through a series of steps.

**1 Conduct market research to find out customer expectations**. The standard for 'quality' is set by the customer, who is therefore the best place to start.

**2 Introduce relevant training in customer service into the organisation.** Any quality initiative needs a skilled workforce, so training is essential.

**3 Set up quality procedures and set quality standards.** This allows a business to set targets and put in place ways of achieving these targets.

**4 Monitor performance against these standards and improve where necessary.** Regular monitoring ensures that the business is still meeting the standards that it has set.

## Benefits of high levels of customer service

These are largely the same as those arising from providing high quality, noted earlier:
- a higher sales volume
- creating a unique selling point (USP)
- a higher selling price
- a better reputation

Additional benefits include:
- a happier working environment
- reduced costs because there are fewer complaints to handle
- possible new contracts resulting from the testimony of satisfied customers
- use of positive publicity for public relations

## Questions

**Read the following passage and answer the questions that follow.**

> Kathryn had inherited the costume hire shop from her mother. The business prided itself on the quality of its customer service. Customer expectations were mainly focused on variety of choice and prompt delivery. As the clothes were only hired for a day, customers were less concerned about the quality of the material than about the appearance of the garment.
>
> Kathryn was constantly surprised by the prices people were prepared to pay, particularly if they had been unable to find a particular outfit elsewhere. Kathryn and her sisters were gifted costume-makers and were able to produce almost any costume at remarkable speed.
>
> Kathryn had worked in her mother's costume hire shop while studying for her A-levels and had learned a lot about what customers wanted. Her mother had always asked customers to complete a questionnaire about the customer service provided and Kathryn kept this approach when she took over the business. The major strength of the business was the fact that the four sisters had all been well trained in costume making by their mother.
>
> All of the sisters loved their jobs and, although the business never advertised, there were regular customers who kept returning and brought in new customers through word-of-mouth.

**1** Identify three examples of customer expectations in the passage.

_____

_____

_____

**2** Briefly explain two main difficulties facing a costume hire shop when trying to provide good customer service.

_____

_____

**3** The four main methods of meeting customer expectations are considered to be market research, training, establishing quality procedures and monitoring performance. To what extent did Kathryn's costume hire shop benefit from applying these four methods to the business?

_____

_____

_____

_____

_____

# Working with suppliers

A **supplier** is an organisation that provides a business with the materials that it needs in order to carry out its business activities.

## Choosing effective suppliers

A business may improve its efficiency to a large extent by choosing effective suppliers. The main factors that a business will consider when choosing a supplier are as follows:

- **Prices.** If the supplier offers low prices, the business benefits because it can reduce the final selling price of its own product and sell more, or it can keep its final selling price the same, but enjoy the benefit of higher added value.
- **Payment terms.** Buyers will want a credit period from a supplier to help their cash flow.
- **Quality.** This is becoming more and more important in the business world. High-quality raw materials will help a business to compete.
- **Capacity.** An organisation will need to be reassured that a supplier has enough capacity to meet the quantity of supply that it requires.
- **Reliability.** This is the extent to which the supplier meets the requirements of the buyer. Typically it can be measured by the percentage of deliveries on time or the degree to which a supplier meets the terms of the contract to supply. Reliability is particularly important if **just-in-time** is used, where items of stock arrive just before production or sale.
- **Flexibility.** There may be situations where an organisation needs radically to change its orders from suppliers and therefore the flexibility of the supplier is vital. Examples are sudden changes in demand for a product and transport difficulties preventing the delivery of supplies from other sources.

## The role of suppliers in improving operational performance

The supplier can have a crucial influence on the achievement of the main operational targets of a business:

- **Unit costs.** The price charged by the supplier is a very important factor that might reduce unit costs and therefore improve operational performance.
- **Quality.** This operational target will be met by the buyer of the materials being supplied.
- **Capacity utilisation**. A buyer will want its suppliers to have the capacity to supply, the reliability to maintain supply at all times, and the flexibility to adjust the level of supply to meet the needs of the buying organisation.

## Questions

1 Explain two ways in which a supplier might influence the unit costs of a business.

........................................................................................................................................................

........................................................................................................................................................

*(Continued overleaf)*

2 Explain how the capacity utilisation of a business might be affected by its suppliers.

**Read the following passage and answer the question that follows.**

Hickson plc was expanding rapidly. It manufactured components for heating systems and a patent had enabled it to increase its market share considerably.

At first, Hickson's expansion led to cash-flow problems. In part this was caused by the decision of its main supplier, Frentzen, to increase its prices when it recognised that Hickson needed its components desperately and could afford to pay more. However, Frentzen did also offer generous credit terms to Hickson, which helped Hickson to avoid further cash shortages.

Most of Hickson's work involved emergency heating repairs, so it was absolutely crucial that components were available at short notice. Frentzen had always been able to provide Hickson with new stock on demand. Furthermore, Frentzen's quality was always so high that there were never any problems of breakdown in heating systems using these components.

Frentzen started using subcontractors to supply some components. Although reliability was still high, the quality of these materials caused problems, as some heating systems broke down.

3 To what extent did Frentzen influence the operational efficiency of Hickson?

# Using technology in operations

In a business context, **technology** describes the applications of practical, mechanical, electrical and related sciences to industry and commerce.

## Robotics

Industrial robots can be programmed to carry out both routine and increasingly complex activities. Some of the main applications of robotics are:

- handling operations and assembling
- welding
- painting and coating materials
- dispensing liquids
- packaging and palletising
- measurement, inspection and testing
- working under hazardous conditions

## Automation

**Computer-aided manufacture** (CAM) is the use of computers to undertake activities such as planning, operating and controlling production.

Technology also helps stock control by enabling businesses to reorder stock automatically, keep an accurate record of stock levels and locate where stock is being held.

## Communications

**Information and communication technology** (ICT) is the acquisition, processing, storage and dissemination of vocal, pictorial, textual and numerical information by a microelectronics-based combination of computing and telecommunications.

## Design

**Computer-aided design** (CAD) is the use of computers to improve the design of products. This can also include programmes to simulate testing, such as wind tunnel simulations, saving considerable sums of money during testing procedures.

**CADCAM** is an approach that combines computer-aided design and computer-aided manufacture, using IT to aid both the design and the manufacture of an item.

## Benefits of using technology in operations

Using technology offers businesses many benefits. First, it helps to **reduce costs**:

- It saves wage costs by reducing jobs.
- It can be used to devise the most cost-effective way of manufacturing a product.
- Use of the internet enables businesses to locate away from expensive sites.

Second, technology **improves quality**:
- Computer-based quality assurance systems can reduce human error.
- ICT gives business a fuller understanding of customers' requirements.

Third, it **reduces waste**:
- Stock control systems ensure that orders are placed at the most appropriate time so that excessive stock levels do not build up.
- Integrated systems of stock control can also identify branches holding stock that is needed by other branches, thereby reducing unsold stock.

Fourth, technology **increases productivity**:
- Machines can work much faster than workers.
- Computerised systems allow organisations to keep much closer control over their stock levels.
- ICT may be used to plan the most efficient approach to production.

Technology also offers **other benefits**:
- The adaptability of technology is now enabling businesses to provide an immediate response to consumers' demands.
- ICT greatly improves financial monitoring and the budgeting process.
- New and higher-quality products can be produced.
- Working conditions may improve.

# Issues in introducing and updating technology

The use of new technology can also cause problems.
- Technology can lead to job losses for workers in traditional skilled crafts.
- Technology can undermine group morale by breaking up teams.
- Technology can be expensive to introduce.
- There is a constant need to update technology and to provide continuous training for staff.

## Questions

**Read the following passage and answer the questions that follow.**

2009 had started badly for Marius. His business, Marius and Co., had introduced a fully automated production line, with robots carrying out all of the stages of production.

The business used CAD and EPOS techniques, to improve design and stock control. When these systems had been introduced, the business had suffered setbacks in the early stages, but Marius was convinced that the business had learned from these earlier difficulties.

Marius had mixed feelings about introducing robotics. The previous changes had led to some job losses, but the automated production line meant that half the company's workforce was made redundant on 31 December 2008.

For the first 3 months of the year there was chaos in the factory, but as time passed matters seemed to improve. Marius had just received the official operational data and wanted to see if it confirmed his view that the introduction of the new technology in January 2009 had caused problems initially but had then led to large improvements in performance.

*Operational data for Marius and Co., 2008–09*

| | 2008 | January to March 2009 | April 2009 onwards |
|---|---|---|---|
| Unit costs (£) | 4.75 | 5.30 | 4.30 |
| Quality: customer satisfaction rating* | 8.9 | 5.0 | 7.6 |
| Waste (%) | 1.8 | 4.6 | 0.3 |
| Weekly output per person | 21 | 18 | 24 |
| *10 = maximum rating; 1 = minimum rating | | | |

1 Analyse the ways in which the introduction of robots and automation can improve the operational efficiency of Marius and Co.

2 Analyse two reasons why it was so difficult for Marius and Co. to avoid short-term problems, despite having had previous experience of introducing technological change in the business.

3 Does the table confirm Marius's view that new technology will worsen matters in the short term before eventually leading to significant improvements in operational efficiency? Justify your view.

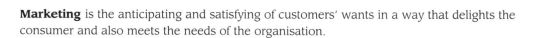

# Effective marketing

**Marketing** is the anticipating and satisfying of customers' wants in a way that delights the consumer and also meets the needs of the organisation.

## The purposes of marketing

The purposes of marketing are:
- anticipating customers' wants, through market research
- satisfying customer wants in a way that delights customers, using a suitable marketing mix
- meeting the needs of the organisation, usually in terms of a profit or growth target

Specifically, the business will set marketing objectives — these are the goals of the marketing function within an organisation.

## Consumer marketing and business-to-business marketing

**Consumer marketing** occurs when a business aims its products at individual consumers.

**Business-to-business marketing** occurs when a business aims its products at individual consumers. The main features of business-to-business marketing are as follows:
- Transactions are much larger.
- Buyers and sellers are specialist employees and have much greater knowledge and under-standing.
- There is much greater emphasis on factors such as after-sales servicing and maintenance.
- Promotions tend to be much more informative rather than persuasive.

## Niche and mass marketing

**Niche marketing** is targeting a product or service at a small segment of a larger market.

**Mass marketing** is aiming a product at all (or most) of the market.

Advantages of niche marketing are:
- There may be fewer competitors.
- The lack of scope for bulk buying may enable small firms to be competitive.
- The limited demand may suit a small firm that lacks the resources to produce on a large scale.
- A firm can adapt its product to meet the specific needs of the niche market, giving it a USP.
- It can be easier for firms to target customers and promote their products effectively when they are only selling to a certain type of customer.

Advantages of mass marketing are:

- Large-scale production is possible, which will help to lower costs per unit.
- The sheer volume of customers enables companies to earn huge revenues.
- Mass marketing allows firms to use the best marketing methods.
- A mass market may provide the funds needed for research and development.

## Questions

1 Define the term 'marketing'.

..............................................................................................................................

..............................................................................................................................

..............................................................................................................................

2 What are the purposes of marketing?

..............................................................................................................................

..............................................................................................................................

..............................................................................................................................

**Read the following passage and answer the questions that follow.**

Nina was excited about her new healthy snack range.

She had planned her business carefully. Her market research had initially consisted of just asking her friends, but as her target market had been young women aged 16–25 their answers had proved to be very relevant. As a result of her market research, Nina set herself three targets:
- annual growth in sales of £50,000 per year for the first 3 years
- the introduction of at least seven new products each year
- a 25% market share for healthy snacks bought by young women aged 16–25 in her town

After 3 years, Nina had met all three targets.

Nina had been very successful at selling her products nationally, advertising her website in some women's magazines. However, the costs of delivering individual items restricted the profit made from this approach.

Instead Nina decided to investigate 'business-to-business' marketing. She approached some national health food stores and they expressed an interest in stocking her range of healthy snacks throughout the country. However, they wanted the products to appeal to the mass market and were concerned that Nina's designs, packaging and advertising were too narrowly focused on appealing to young women.

Nina had made a good profit every year to date, but would need to borrow a lot of money to move into the mass market.

3 Did Nina set appropriate marketing objectives?

4 Analyse two benefits to Nina from concentrating on a niche market.

5 Examine how Nina's marketing will change if she focuses on business-to-business marketing rather than her current consumer marketing approach.

6 Discuss whether Nina should change from a niche market to a mass market approach.

# Using the marketing mix: product

The section on 'Designing an effective marketing mix' has been placed on pp. 76–77, so that you have tackled the material on the marketing mix (the four Ps) before examining how these elements can be integrated to create an effective marketing mix.

## The development of new products

A **product** is a good or service provided by a business

Every new product or service will pass through certain stages before it is launched. The stages of new product development are as follows:
1 Generation of ideas
2 Analysis of ideas
3 Product development
4 Test marketing *(not always used)*
5 Launch

## Influences on the development of new goods and services

The development of new goods and services is influenced by several factors.

**Technology**
- New technology can create new products that are superior to existing products.
- Production and process technology have reduced production costs.
- Technology has enabled businesses to produce services (and goods) that are made to the individual specifications of the consumer.
- Technology allows companies to have a better understanding of their consumers' views.

**Competitors' actions**
- A new product from a competitor may take away a firm's market share.
- New products from competitors can give a business ideas for its own new products. Changes in consumer tastes may be detected through the actions of a competitor. This may lead to an organisation introducing new products.

**Entrepreneurial skills of managers and owners**
- New products occur because an entrepreneur identifies an opportunity.
- Many organisations encourage and reward managers who come up with innovative ideas.
- New products also arise from research and development.

**Other factors**
- Market research.
- Ideas from other countries.
- Personal experience and personal inventiveness.

# Unique selling points

The **unique selling point** or proposition (USP) describes those features of a product or service that allow it to be differentiated from other products. Methods of creating a USP through marketing include:

- developing a popular brand name through promotions
- modifying a product to attract new market segments
- attractive packaging
- enhanced customer service, such as providing tailor-made products

# Product portfolio analysis

The range of products a business provides is its **product portfolio**. The **Boston matrix** is a popular method of product portfolio analysis.

The different types of product identified in the Boston matrix are:

- **Stars.** These are products with a high percentage market share in a high-growth market.
- **Cash cows.** These products have a high percentage market share in a low-growth market.
- **Problem children** (also known as 'question marks' or 'wildcats'). These are goods with a low percentage market share in a high-growth market.
- **Dogs.** These are goods with a low percentage market share in a low-growth market.

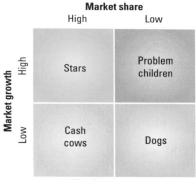

*The Boston matrix*

On balance, a firm would prefer a portfolio of cash cows and stars. However, dogs can be profitable and a problem child might become a cash cow in the future.

# Product life cycle

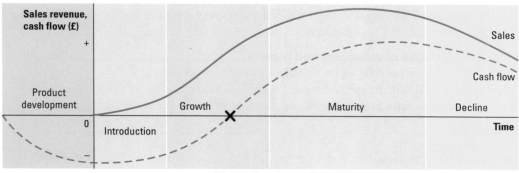

*The product life cycle*

The **product life cycle** shows the stages that a product passes through during its lifetime. These stages are:
- development
- introduction
- growth
- maturity
- decline

In theory, a firm should aim to have as many products in 'maturity' as possible, as these are the products that should generate most profit. However, to achieve this in the long run a firm needs to have a policy of new product development, so that it has products in the introduction and growth stages which will eventually enter maturity.

**Extension strategies** are used to lengthen the life cycle of a product by preventing it from reaching the decline stage. The main extension strategies are:
- attracting new market segments
- increasing usage among existing customers
- modifying the product
- changing the image
- targeting new markets
- promotions, advertising and price offers

## Questions

1 a Identify three factors that influence the introduction of new products.

b Select any product or service that has been recently introduced and explain how **one** of the factors identified in part (a) influenced its introduction.

2 a What is meant by the term 'USP'?

b Give a real-life example of a USP for a product of your choice.

**Study the table below and answer the questions that follow.**

*Market information on five products produced by LBW plc*

| | Annual % growth in sales of product (last 3 years) | | | Annual % growth in sales of market as a whole | Market share (%) |
|---|---|---|---|---|---|
| Product A | +3 | 0 | +1 | +1 | 40 |
| Product B | – | – | * | +33 | 2 |
| Product C | – | +16 | +18 | +3 | 7 |
| Product D | –2 | –5 | –18 | –5 | 8 |
| Product E | +25 | +32 | +32 | +19 | 44 |

*Product just launched, so annual figures not yet available.

3 In the Boston matrix, in which category would you place each product?

a Product A

b Product B

c Product C

d Product D

e Product E

4 In which stage of the product life cycle would you place each product?

a Product A

b Product B

c Product C

d Product D

e Product E

5 Select any two of the five products listed and evaluate how LBW plc might use your answers to questions 3 and 4 in deciding how to market them.

# Using the marketing mix: promotion

**Promotion** is the process of communicating with customers or potential customers.

**Advertising** is the process of communicating with customers or potential customers through specific media, such as television and newspapers.

**Informative promotion** is intended to increase consumer awareness of the product and its features.

**Persuasive promotion** is intended to encourage consumers to purchase the product, usually through messages that emphasise its desirability.

## Elements of the promotional mix

Types of promotion include:
- **Public relations (PR).** PR involves gaining favourable publicity through the media.
- **Branding.** This is the process of differentiating a product or service from its competitors through the name, sign, symbol, design or slogan linked to that product.
- **Merchandising.** Attempts to persuade consumers to take action at the 'point of sale' (PoS), also known as the 'point of purchase' (PoP), are known as merchandising.
- **Sales promotions.** These are short-term incentives used to persuade consumers to purchase. Popular methods include competitions, free offers, coupons, 'three for the price of two' or BOGOF (buy one, get one free) offers, introductory offers, product placement (featuring a product in a film), credit terms and endorsements by famous personalities.
- **Direct selling.** This takes three main forms: direct mail, telephone selling and door-to-door drops.
- **Advertising.** The main media chosen are television, radio, cinema, newspapers (national and regional), magazines, posters, the internet and other electronic media.

## Influences on the choice of promotional mix

When deciding on its promotion activities, a business will consider the following factors:
- objectives of the campaign
- costs and budgets
- the target market
- the need for a mixture of different promotions within a campaign
- legal factors
- external factors, such as the state of the economy

## Questions

1 Explain two factors that influence the promotional mix of a product.

...............................................................................................................................

...............................................................................................................................

...............................................................................................................................

**Read the following passage and answer the questions that follow.**

David had just taken over his father's business. The business had been neglected in recent years, although two of its products were unique because they were patented and still sold well.

The first product — a can and bottle opener — was sold nationally in many large stores, but some stores had stopped stocking it in recent years because competitors had organised successful promotions.

The second product — a multipurpose workbench — was sold directly to customers in the area around David's home town of Portsmouth. David had considered selling it directly to customers nationally, as it had a high value added, but it was expensive to transport.

2 Analyse the reasons why David should use a mixture of informative promotion and persuasive promotion.

3 Evaluate the reasons why David should use a different promotional mix for the workbench than that used for the can and bottle opener.

# Using the marketing mix: pricing

## Pricing strategies and tactics

**Pricing strategies** are adopted in order to achieve marketing objectives. There are four main pricing strategies.

- **Price skimming** is a strategy in which a high price is set to yield a high profit margin.
- **Penetration pricing** is a strategy in which low prices are set to break into a market or to achieve a sudden spurt in market share.
- **Price leadership** involves large companies setting a market price that smaller firms will tend to follow.
- **Price taking** involves small firms following the price set by a price leader.

**Pricing tactics** are adopted in the short term to suit particular situations. There are two main pricing tactics:

- **loss leadership** — a tactic in which a firm sets a very low price for its product(s) in order to encourage consumers to buy other products
- **psychological pricing** — a tactic intended to give the impression of value (e.g. selling a good for £9.99 rather than £10)

There are two main influences on the pricing decision:
- the costs of production
- price elasticity of demand

## Costs of production

Usually a business needs to ensure that it makes a profit, so the price of a product must be set in order to cover costs.

**Cost-plus pricing** is a method of pricing in which the price set is the average cost of a product plus a sum to ensure a profit. The percentage added on will depend on:
- the level of competition
- the price that customers are prepared to pay
- the firm's objectives — for example, whether it is aiming to break even or maximise profit, or to achieve a high market share.

## Price elasticity of demand

**Price elasticity of demand** is the responsiveness of a change in the quantity demanded of a good or service to a change in price. The formula for calculating the price elasticity of demand is as follows:

$$\text{price elasticity of demand} = \frac{\% \text{ change in quantity demanded}}{\% \text{ change in price}}$$

Price elasticity of demand is usually elastic or inelastic.
- **Elastic demand.** Demand is elastic if the percentage change in price leads to a greater percentage change in the quantity demanded. The numerical value will be >1.

- **Inelastic demand.** Demand is inelastic if the percentage change in price leads to a smaller percentage change in the quantity demanded. The numerical value will be <1.

Factors influencing the price elasticity of demand are:

- necessity
- habit
- availability of substitutes
- brand loyalty
- the proportion of income spent on a product
- income of consumers

If demand for a good is *inelastic*, when its price rises the quantity demanded falls by a smaller percentage. This means that if price increases, sales revenue will increase. But if price falls, sales revenue will fall.

If demand for a good is *elastic*, when its price rises the quantity demanded falls by a larger percentage. This means that if price increases, sales revenue will decrease. But if price falls, sales revenue will rise.

There are several difficulties in using price elasticity of demand:

- There may have been significant changes in the market, affecting the level of demand independently of price. For example, consumer tastes may have changed; new competitors may have entered the market; technological change may have influenced the market; or the image of the product may have changed.
- Changes in price may provoke rival firms to match the change.
- Consumers may be unable to predict how their spending will be affected by price changes, so primary surveys may be unreliable.

## Questions

**Read the following passage and answer the questions that follow.**

Lara's pharmaceutical supplies business was thriving. When she had first started up, she had struggled to make a profit because copying the prices of the large, established suppliers did not leave enough money for a decent profit.

Her big breakthrough came when some major pharmaceutical retailers agreed to stock 'Curius', a product that she imported from Germany. There were no similar products provided by rival UK suppliers. Matters improved further when medical research proved that this product was the best cure for a major illness. Lara had a 5-year deal with the German manufacturer to be the sole supplier in the UK.

Her other big seller was toilet rolls. A Chinese supplier had contacted her, hoping to gain entry into the UK market. The costs of the toilet rolls were so low that Lara and the retailers were able to make a decent profit and yet still compete with supermarket prices.

The price elasticity of demand for toilet rolls was very elastic and both Lara and the retailers had benefited a great deal from lowering the price.

1 What pricing strategy did Lara use when she first started up? Explain your reasoning.

2 What type of pricing strategy should Lara use for Curius? Justify your choice.

3 Explain why the price elasticity of demand for Curius is likely to be inelastic.

4 Analyse why toilet rolls are often sold as loss leaders by retailers.

5 Analyse why psychological pricing might be used for toilet rolls.

6 Other than their use as a loss leader, explain why retailers would benefit from lowering the price of toilet rolls.

.......................................................................................................................................................

.......................................................................................................................................................

.......................................................................................................................................................

.......................................................................................................................................................

.......................................................................................................................................................

.......................................................................................................................................................

7 'The price elasticity of demand for necessities is usually inelastic.'

'Toilet rolls are a necessity.'

'The price elasticity of demand for toilet rolls is elastic.'

Discuss the reasons for these apparent contradictions.

.......................................................................................................................................................

.......................................................................................................................................................

.......................................................................................................................................................

.......................................................................................................................................................

.......................................................................................................................................................

.......................................................................................................................................................

.......................................................................................................................................................

.......................................................................................................................................................

.......................................................................................................................................................

# Using the marketing mix: place

## The importance of location

Making sure that the business operates in the right location involves several elements:
- **Convenience.** Customers want to be close to the place of purchase.
- **Accessibility.** The place of purchase must be easy to get to by usual forms of transport.
- **Cost of access.** The lower the cost, the better.
- **Reputation.** For a few products, the address of the location can enhance the organisation's reputation.
- **Localisation.** Some retailers tend to locate close to competition for consumer convenience.

## Placement within the point of sale

Market research into groceries indicates that 70% of buying decisions are made in-store. Consequently, sales of products can be increased by the careful placing of products within the point-of-sale outlet. Some examples are:
- Similar products (e.g. biscuits) are placed together, so that shoppers can make comparisons.
- Brightly coloured, fresh produce is made visible from outside the store.
- Impulse buys (e.g. sweets) are put close to the checkouts.
- Popular products are given greater shelf space.
- Loss leaders are scattered around the store, to encourage shoppers to visit the whole store.

## The number of outlets

Manufacturers try to widen the number of outlets stocking their products through:
- promotional campaigns to boost demand
- providing extra facilities or attractive displays for retailers to use
- offering high profit margins to retailers

## Types of distribution channel

Distribution channels are the routes through which a product passes in moving from the manufacturer (producer) to the consumer.

Most domestic distribution involves one of three methods, as shown in the diagram.

| Traditional | Modern | Direct |
|---|---|---|
| Producer | Producer | Producer |
| ↓ | ↓ | ↓ |
| Wholesaler | | |
| ↓ | Retailer | |
| Retailer | ↓ | |
| ↓ | | |
| Consumer | Consumer | Consumer |

*Channels of distribution*

## Factors influencing the method of distribution

The final choice of distribution channel depends on the following:
- **Size of the retailer.** Large retailers may want to bypass the wholesaler.
- **Type of product.** For a perishable product being sent to a limited number of retailers, it may be desirable to bypass the wholesaler.

- **Number of retailers.** If many retailers are used, it is usually more economical to use a wholesaler to deliver to retailers.
- **Technology.** More products are now being sold directly through the internet.
- **Geography of the market.** In a remote rural area, it is less likely to be cost-effective for a manufacturer (producer) to deliver directly.
- **Complexity of the product.** The product may need direct contact with the producer or an expert retailer.
- **Degree of control desired by the manufacturer.** In order to protect their reputation, some firms will deliver directly to selected retailers only.

## Questions

**1** Show three different types of channels of distribution.

.........................................................................................................................................

.........................................................................................................................................

.........................................................................................................................................

**2** Briefly explain two factors that would make a specific location desirable for a supermarket.

.........................................................................................................................................

.........................................................................................................................................

.........................................................................................................................................

**Read the following passage and answer the questions that follow.**

Fernando looked at his latest sales figures. Six years ago he had owned a thriving wholesale business in Barton. About 75% of his sales had come from groceries, but the opening of two major supermarkets in the town had led to a massive cut in his sales.

It was fortunate that he had diversified into building supplies, as these now accounted for the majority of his sales. Fernando offered credit terms to local tradesmen who bought his products.

Fernando had acquired a reputation as a DIY expert and this attracted many individual customers who were prepared to pay higher prices because they knew that Fernando would sell them the right product for their home repairs.

Fernando had tried to persuade supermarket customers to buy products directly, as his warehouse contained large boxes of a range of products that was almost as wide as the range stocked by a typical supermarket. However, despite a great deal of advertising he had been unable to persuade people to do their grocery shopping in his warehouse.

He wondered if there was anything more that he could do to revive the business.

3 Examine why the opening of two retail supermarkets would damage the sales of a wholesaler, such as Fernando.

4 Advise Fernando on one action that he could take to revive his business, giving reasons for your advice.

5 Evaluate possible reasons why Fernando has been able to achieve success in DIY products.

# Designing an effective marketing mix

The **marketing mix** comprises those elements of a firm's approach to marketing that enable it to satisfy and delight its customers.

There are three main influences on the marketing mix: finance, technology and market research.

## Finance

As marketing involves significant expenditure before any results are achieved, and will always include an element of risk, the finances of a firm are critical.
- If a business has cash-flow problems, it may need to reduce spending on promotion.
- Is the firm able to buy raw materials at a discounted price?
- What is the marketing budget and what is the cost of promotions?

## Technology

- If a product is technologically advanced, it will usually be more popular with customers.
- If a business has a sophisticated database with information on specific customers, it is more likely to use direct mail or internet contact to attract them.
- Technology helps organisations to produce high quality at low costs.
- New technology in the form of the internet is having a major impact on the 'place' element of the marketing mix.

## Market research

- If market research shows the existence of a lot of competition, a business needs to differentiate its product from those of competitors.
- Continuous market research is required to keep up-to-date with markets.
- Market research will reveal the best market segments to target and the best media to use to reach those segments.

## The importance of an integrated marketing mix

A good marketing mix needs to be coordinated so that each element supports the other parts of the mix. Some examples of the importance of an integrated marketing mix are:
- If the main selling point of a product is its excellence, the quality, design and price of that product must match consumers' expectations.
- Promotion is often designed to draw attention to other features of the marketing mix, such as price, place or the product design.
- Efficient distribution (place) may enable a firm to keep costs and prices low. The point-of-sale can be used to show the product and to promote it, through posters.
- For impulse buys, place is vital but promotion is needed to make customers recognise the product, and the product design must attract attention.

## Questions

**1** Select any product with which you are familiar and show how its marketing mix might be influenced by:

**a** finance

_____

_____

_____

_____

**b** technology

_____

_____

_____

_____

**c** market research

_____

_____

_____

_____

**2** Selecting a _different_ product from that chosen in question 1, evaluate the relative importance of each of the four Ps in its marketing mix.

_____

_____

_____

_____

_____

_____

_____

# Marketing and competitiveness

A **market** is a place where buyers and sellers come together.

## Market structure and the degree of competition

In general, four different market structures explain the broad range of competitive environments in which most firms operate.
- **Monopoly** — in theory, a single producer within a market, but in practice a firm with a market share of 25% or more.
- **Oligopoly** — a market dominated by a small number of large firms.
- **Monopolistic competition** — a large number of firms competing within a market, each having enough product differentiation to achieve a degree of monopoly power and therefore some control over the price it charges.
- **Perfect competition** — a large number of sellers and buyers, all of which are too small to influence the price of the product. All sellers produce homogeneous (identical) products.

## The impact of market conditions on the marketing mix

Each of the above market structures has a different impact on the marketing mix.
- **Monopoly** — the lack of competition means that little needs to be spent on marketing and a high price can be charged.
- **Oligopoly** — oligopolists typically focus on product design and promotion to differentiate their products from competition.
- **Monopolistic competition** — product differentiation is vital, although place can also be vital.
- **Perfect competition** — products are identical, so place is arguably the vital element.

## Competitiveness

**Competitiveness** is the ability of firms to sell their products successfully within the market in which they are based.

Major determinants of competitiveness include:
- investment in new equipment and technology
- staff skills, education and training
- innovation through investment in research and development
- enterprise and the entrepreneurial skills of business owners
- the effectiveness of the marketing mix
- incentive schemes for staff
- improvements in operations management
- quality procedures
- effective financial planning and control

Methods of improving competitiveness include:
* marketing
* reducing costs
* improving quality
* staff training

## Questions

**1** What is the difference between the market structures described as 'perfect competition' and 'monopolistic competition'?

<br>
<br>
<br>
<br>

**Read the following passage and answer the questions that follow.**

Yvonne was worried. As managing director of Super-Clean plc, a manufacturer of cleaning products, she was concerned that two of her company's leading products had suffered a fall in sales over the last 12 months.

She examined the summary that her fellow directors had provided for each product.

| Product name | Main features | Strengths | Weaknesses |
|---|---|---|---|
| Brillio | Dishwasher powder | Newly patented idea<br>High-quality reputation<br>Wide variety of colours<br>3% market share | Low marketing budget<br>Low price/profit<br>High unit costs |
| Graze | Antiseptic wipe | High price/profit<br>Well-known brand<br>Cash cow<br>45% market share | High labour turnover in factory<br>Inconsistent quality<br>Old-fashioned image |

**2** Brillio and Graze are both differentiated from competitors' products. Identify the market structure in which each product operates.

<br>
<br>

**3** Analyse three reasons why Graze may have suffered a loss in sales.

_____

_____

_____

_____

_____

_____

_____

_____

_____

_____

_____

**4** Advise Yvonne on how Super-Clean plc might improve the competitiveness of Brillio. Justify your advice.

_____

_____

_____

_____

_____

_____

_____

_____

_____

_____

_____

_____

_____

_____

_____

_____

_____